When the heart is full, the eyes overflow.

—Yiddish proverb

Knock-Your-Socks-Off Art and Literature

www.kysoflash.com

KYSO Flash online journal

KYSO Flash Press

My Dharma Box

New and Selected Writings by

Dan Gilmore

My Dharma Box: New and Selected Writings
By Dan Gilmore

ISBN: 978-0-9862703-9-0

Edited and published by Clare MacQueen
KYSO Flash Press; Seattle, WA, USA: April 2018

Please send questions and comments to:

KYSOWebmaster@gmail.com

Dedicated to my life partner, JoAn

Other Books by Dan Gilmore:

New Shoes: New and Selected Haibun Stories
With cover art by Gwen Murphy
(KYSO Flash Press, 2016)

Just Before Sleep: Haibun Stories
(KYSO Flash Press, 2015)

Panning for Gold: New and Selected Poems
(Imago Press, 2014)

Love Takes a Bow: New and Selected Poems
(Imago Press, 2010)

A Howl for Mayflower
(Imago Press, 2006)

Season Tickets: Poems and Stories
(Pima Press, 2003)

Table of Contents

Intro From the Publisher

Maybe you've heard of the "dharma box." It's a Buddhist idea, explained in more detail in Anyen Rinpoche's book *Dying With Confidence: A Tibetan Buddhist Guide to Preparing for Death*. Basically, the dharma box is a container which holds treasured items, such as photographs of loved ones, keepsakes, sacred objects, and/or special writings like prayers, poems, letters, a spiritual will and testament, etc., that will help family and friends support a person during his or her end-of-life transition.

This book you're holding, this collection of endearing, enlightened, and entertaining writings, is itself Dan Gilmore's dharma box. Dan is an 81-year-old poet, fiction writer, and cherished friend of mine who received a terminal diagnosis late last year. As he wrote to me in January 2018, this book has lots to say about life and death, especially after we've become death-conscious. Each of the 50 works herein contains something that Dan believes will make his dying more pleasant. And just after this intro, you'll find a list of more than a hundred folks, alive and dead, whom he's inviting to his "Dharma Box Party" to help support his dying process.

While designing the covers of this book, I considered images of several square and rectangular boxes—but as soon as I saw the heart-shaped box that now appears on the front cover, it seemed perfect. Dan agreed, as it's spiritually meaningful to both of us.

As he wrote in an earlier email (November 2017): "It's increasing clear to me that the ONLY thing that makes sense anymore is love. The head is willful, self-indulgent, judgemental, demanding, needy, and often wrong. The heart is compassionate, grateful, tolerant, empathetic, patient, and always right..."

My Dharma Box is Dan's sixth collection of poems and stories. He's also the author of a novel. Not surprisingly, 81 years on the planet have blessed him with an abundance of rich material to draw from. Beyond a myriad of roles as son, brother, spouse, life partner, friend, father, and grandfather, his life experiences include blue-, white-, and gold-collar jobs from (among others) fry cook to college dean to psychologist. Plus, ongoing work as a no-collar jazz musician and creative writer, who's been creating poetry and fiction for more than 20 years now.

"Writing this book has been like chasing butterflies," Dan says. "End-of-life is loaded with new discoveries, some scary but most, delightful. My dog, Molly, and a crippled cricket have become amazing teachers. Tomatoes are patient. I miss ice-fishing in Minnesota although I have never been fishing anywhere. And all of it goes into my dharma box" (from email, 22 February 2018).

As the publisher, it's my privilege, my honor, and my great pleasure to present to you this gift of Dan's wise and witty words. And to Dan, I offer my heartfelt gratitude for his contributions to KYSO Flash, which have been legion, and for his steadfast encouragement "to do good work in the world."

As Pericles said so long ago, "What you leave behind is not what is engraved in stone monuments, but what is woven into the lives of others."*

Thank you, Dan, for giving us so much to weave into our lives! Peaceful passage, my dear friend. God be with you.

—Clare MacQueen
(April, 2018)

*[*See Footnote I, page 79.]*

Guest List for My Dharma Box Party

JoAn Forehand, Willard Day, Fifi Day, Sam Day, Mayflower, Cheryl Seaton, Carol Ann Lee, George Jay, Hattie Bell Gilmore, Thurman Gilmore, Bill Martin, Lisa Martin, Tom Speer, Steve Kowit, Clare MacQueen, Alan Rubins, Roy Phillips, Patricia Harmon, S. L. Holland, Jane Ellen Thompson, Linda Hook, Tom McMahon, Mike DeBellis, Conrad Driussi, Jennifer Gilmore, Jeff Seminoff, Quin Seminoff, Graeson Seminoff, Peggy Duncan, David Tyler, Danny Douglas Gilmore, Leo Gilmore, Lucy Gilmore, Ada Jo Gilmore, Amanda Gilmore, Raymond Carver, Chekhov, Virginia Hall, Virginia Wolfe, James Hillman, Robert Bly, Ellen Bass, Cam Wilson, Tobias Seltzer, Karen DeLay, Bill Sandell, Bill Bucci, Nan Rubins, David Van Houten, Jackie Newlove, Holly Jebb, Janet Smith, Audrey Lee Fatola, Duncan Scott, Frederick Eisele, Jamie Mitchell, Ted Kooser, Kathleen Roberts, Margaret Dykinga, Mary Norman, Cynthia Meier, Stella Miles, Trudy Hill, Meg Hovel, Nancy Wall, Bobby Shechtman, Ronny Ossa, Joe Hofmeister, Rafael Bejarano, Bob Fosse, Marilyn Civer, Ram Dass, Karen DeBellis, Lillian Fisher, Masha Hamilton, Carl Rogers, Dorianne Laux, Sam Lawrence, Heather Lindsley, Bob Longoni, Terryl Mack, Joe McGrath, Andrew Periele, Dan Wolfe, Bernadette Steel, Edward Albee, Samuel Beckett, Duncan Littlefair, Allen Ginsberg, Fritz Perls, B. F. Skinner, John Kautz, Lou Andreas Salome, Billie Holiday, Willy Loman, Chief Bromden, Zorba, Walt Whitman, Rumi, Jackson Pollack, Henry Miller, Franz Kline, Hans Hoffman, Willem de Kooning, Picasso, John Lee Hooker, Mozart, The Beatles, Elvis, Janis Joplin, Henry Moore, Dionysius, Hermes, Frida Kahlo, Eleanor Roosevelt, Helen Frankenthaler, Sappho, Vonnegut, Einstein, Frank Lloyd Wright, Julia Childs, and Charles Mingus

---

See pages 84-85 for an alphabetized list.

✧

ALS is the perfect vehicle to learn about death in slow motion,
how it plays with emotions and soul and relationships,
how it challenges basic beliefs, how it holds each minute up
before you and asks, "What do you think of this one?"

—Dan Gilmore
(19 April 2018)

Part I

To every thing there is a season,
and a time to every purpose under heaven:
A time to be born, and a time to die...
a time to weep, and a time to laugh;
a time to mourn, and a time to dance....

Everyone should eat and drink, and enjoy the good
of all their labour: it is the gift of God.

...There is nothing better, that a man should rejoice
in his own works: that is his portion, for who shall
bring him to see what shall be after him?

—From Ecclesiastes 3, *The Holy Bible*

The Gizmo

I got the news in one of those square little rooms with an exam table, a sink, two steel chairs, and a computer. As the doctor talked I held tight to a rolled-up *People* magazine, noticed a place for disposing of syringes, watched the sink's faucet drip slower than the number of months he thought I had left. And when silence came, I couldn't think of what else to say so I said, "Thank you," and he said, "You're welcome."

Driving home, I needed to make a list: will, finances, estate sale; write my autobiography—scratch that; make a video—scratch that; make a few calls. I stopped by Walgreens to buy a pencil and pocket notebook but bought Snickers and Red Vines instead. Stopped at Gus Balone's Cafe. Had three eggs, double bacon, double hash browns, and two biscuits with sausage gravy.

In my kitchen, I opened my junk drawer to look for a note pad and saw that electric gizmo I'd held onto for years, a square thing that plugged into a wall socket. There was a receptacle in the back where something plugged into it, but that part was missing. As far as I knew, it had never existed. But holding that gizmo in my hand, I truly believed that if I could find that missing part and plug it into my gizmo, everything would be okay. I wouldn't die. I'd never die.

✧

The Joy of Being Lost

for JoAn

When I was five, I got lost in the Goodwill, separated from my mother, and how I wandered through the aisles, my heart a jackhammer, a thousand tambourines in my head, the air a thick paste. Too short to see over the aisle dividers, I sat on the cold cement floor, lost in a dark silence. Lost.... Then I heard my mother's voice, looked up, and saw her coming toward me. And I experienced a shutter's glimpse into eternity, a deep knowing that could not be spoken or sustained, but could never be forgotten. For that moment it seemed as though I was the creator of a brighter world, as if I were seeing everything for the first time, the store, the dust floating in the light, my mother, all a joyous new form of life.

I remembered that today when, after my doctor's appointment, you went for a walk in the rain and came in clutching a bouquet of white and purple wildflowers, your hair wet, your smile crooked. I took the bouquet from you and felt found again.

Oinks

We're in Bob's pickup headed for The Oink Café. He knows about my diagnosis, and he's depressed about his girlfriend walking out on him. He says we should try to commit suicide by bacon. I hear the door close on my heart-healthy awareness. For a year I have eaten nothing that ever had a face, avoided anything with even a drop of added fat. Now that I know I have ALS, a disease that's sure to kill me, I think it might be easier to die of a heart attack. So, I've decided to eat lots of bacon, eggs fried in Crisco, popcorn soaked with butter. Last night I ate six Italian sausages dipped in mayonnaise. Bob is talking about Sandra and the guy she went off with. "Bacon is the only answer," he says. I ask about sweets. He says he's going to eat a pound of See's turtles a day. I tell him turtles are good with Cheetos. "You should try them with bacon," he says. By this time, we're at Oink's. We sit at a table with a yellow tablecloth and a daisy on it. Every breath is a bacon breath. The waitress is pretty and happy. "What'll you have, boys?" she says. Music is playing. A tune I don't recognize, but I can't help thinking it's my song.

Confession

When it finally got through to me and I realized that the doctor wasn't messing with my head, I found myself wanting to be...you know—deeper, more honest, compassionate and wise. But it hasn't worked out all that well. For instance, I started yesterday by meditating on the Prayer of St. Francis, but for breakfast I ate fried Spam and eggs, and that afternoon I had a significant wrath-and-fury session while watching the news. After meditating on world peace for a few minutes, I then met a friend for coffee and talked for two hours about the upcoming baseball season. I have some beautiful spiritually-inclined friends, but seem to spend more time with the fleshlier ones. Like Charlie, who just got his new leg because he lost his old one to diabetes, and whose main passion now is watching the news three hours a night to see how that thing with Trump and his porn star turns out.

And so it goes, early morning spirituality, afternoon gluttony, and evening pointlessness. I confess I'll miss pointlessness the most, the cosmic practical joke of it, the humor that makes the days slide by almost unnoticed. At night when my head hits the pillow, I sigh and wonder, *where has the time gone?*

When I Gave Up My Battle Against Hi-Tech

Lately I've been feeling like the world's soul is being consumed by advanced technology and that part of my work before I leave this planet is to free it from the web of digitalization. Sheila was my first target. At the diner where we met for lunch, there's a sign: WE DON'T HAVE WI-FI. TALK TO EACH OTHER. Sheila didn't see it because she was trying to fix her phone. Last week we attended a memorial for our friend Bud, and during the service Bud's daughter checked her phone four times. Sheila didn't notice because she was texting Roger, her boyfriend. After Bud's memorial, we went to Starbucks. It looked like a church service, all heads bowed over phones. Sheila left her "notifications" on, in case Roger wanted to apologize. She said they were having relationship issues, that he likes his phone more than he likes her. I told her that maybe we have become a society where we are connected to everyone but touch no one, a society of delusional relationships grounded on virtual loneliness. *Nailed it!* I thought. But she didn't hear me. She was texting Roger. I told her I'd read that it's now possible, with a special sensory body suit, to have virtual sex which is better than the real thing. She said, "Really? What's the website?"

Ménage a Trois

Life and I were a couple for many years—worked, played, and drank hard. Often promiscuous. Then one day we found ourselves with lower back pain, memory loss, and social security checks. Shortly thereafter, we discovered Death sleeping on the back porch. She was no bother at first. Mostly kept to herself during the day. She seemed to enjoy TV. She laughed out loud when I told her about my long-range plans to move to Phoenix and open a car wash.

Before long the three of us were sleeping together. For hours I lay staring into the darkness. While Death snored, Life tossed a heavy leg over my thigh. And now we go everywhere together. We hold hands and take long meandering walks, me in the center. Death likes walking in the shade, Life in the light. We do a little dance—*dark, light, dark, light.* They're like whining children. I try to keep them both happy.

> *light and shadow dance*
> *the butterfly lingers*
> *over a field of poppies*

Massive Impermanence

On the TV over the bar, the Yankees are playing the Red Sox. A bearded man sits next to me and orders a martini, very dry with three olives. Discriminating, I think. So I order the same. We talk (but not about our health, oddly enough). We both hate the Yankees and airports. Turns out he's a physicist from Cal Tech who is looking for the God particle. I eat one of my olives. "Sounds religious," I say. He finishes off his martini in one gulp, but doesn't touch his olives. "The thing is," he says, "we still can't account for why this bar and these martinis and even you and I have mass. Everything has a sound, the same sound. Everything's in motion, but just why these olives are olives and this gin is gin and garbage is garbage, we don't have a clue. The real question is, why doesn't everything just fall apart? Why don't you and I just vanish, *poof?*"

I consider this and suggest that maybe we should order another martini before we vaporize. "Good idea," he says. So, we toast to our temporary solidity, then I close my eyes for a few seconds to see if I can experience my God particles, those things I am destined to become. And for a moment I'm a part of one big caldron of God soup, and I feel a great kinship with olives, the Yankees, and this Cal Tech physicist. But when I open my eyes the physicist isn't there. He's gone. So has his glass and his left-over olives. I feel a little giddy and happy to be back.

✧

Miracles

for Ted Kooser

Ted and I are drinking beer in the run-down Corner Bar in Garland, Nebraska, population, 210. Fran, the bartender, loses interest when I start giving Ted my take on miracles—the miracle that more of us aren't killed for tweeting when we drive; the miracle that on most days, the majority of us actually find something to eat and safe water to drink. Ted signals Fran for another round as I tell him what a miracle it is that terrorists haven't already set off a bomb at the Super Bowl.

When I pause, he holds up his bottle to the light and tells me about a beer bottle he saw in a burned-out highway ditch. "Tossed from a car," he says. "It had landed straight up, unbroken. Like a cat thrown off a roof that landed hard and stands dazzled in the sun, right side up." He takes a slug of beer. "Sort of a miracle," he says.

And Fran says, "Was that bottle over on Lakeside Road near the Holland bridge?" And Ted says, "Indeed it was."

"That's my bottle," Fran says. "I tossed it out over a week ago. Landed right side up, and still standing, eh?" She looks me in the eye. "Now that's a miracle."

> *perched on a post*
> *raven waits for car and rabbit*
> *to cross paths*

Billie Holiday, July 1959

I sat no more than five feet away, nursing a gin and tonic, poised to leap up and help her if she fell. She sat, unsteady, in a stained blue dress under a smoky white light, only half alive from her last shot of heroin, body ravaged by rape, domestic abuse, racism, imprisonment. With one high-heeled shoe hooked on the stool's crossbar, the other planted on the floor to hold herself steady, she sang "God Bless the Child," "Good Morning Heartache," and "Strange Fruit." It wasn't that velvety voice of a soft fire with warm embers, but the sound of white water in a rocky river. But she refused to give up. Once, when she couldn't hit the note, an angry, deep-throated growl rose up as if she were pleading to God to find the strength to finish the set. There she was, Lady Day, used up but doing what she was born to do up until the end. She died three weeks later. As I battle my own rough waters, I pause to ask God to give me a little of what Lady Day had, her soulful determination to find the right note and to last until the end of the set.

Fame, aka Ginsberg's Last Soup *

This morning I wrote a poem about death. This evening I made some soup. My soup was better than my poem. The broth was deep and rich. I tossed in some chopped carrots, tomatoes, a big zucchini, garlic, basil, rosemary, and onion. The poem was a meditation on how the world might adjust to my loss when I die.

Long ago I was lucky enough to have dinner with Allen Ginsberg. He made soup. He took pride in his soup. He said he'd give me what we didn't eat, and suggested I freeze it in ice cube trays. He said every cube would be worth a lot of money after he died. I thought he was joking.

The last soup Ginsberg made before he died was a complex fish chowder. It contained parsnips, cilantro, tofu, mussels in their shells and fish heads. It's now frozen and on display at the Museum of Jurassic Technology in Los Angeles alongside mouse pie (said to cure stuttering) and an exhibit about sin-eaters (people hired to consume chunks of bread that had been passed over a corpse).

I let my soup simmer for an hour and added some sprigs of thyme and parsley. I dipped chunks of bread in it and ate them while considering the possibility of converting to Judaism. Then I thought, maybe I dwell too long on how the empty space I leave can't possibly be filled. I deleted the poem, froze the leftover soup in ice cube trays, and started a funny poem about mouse pie.

*[*See Footnote II, pages 79-80.]*

Not a Gift of Aging

In handicapped parking at Starbucks, I was trying to pull my walker from my trunk when a beautiful woman came toward me—long blond hair, tight white pants, loose knit white top, stiletto heels. She flashed a devastating smile, all glittery white, framed in crimson red, and for a millisecond the world was good and anything was possible. Snow White and Prince Charming had finally escaped their separate stories and found each other in a Starbucks' parking lot. It was that same rush I felt as a sixth-grader when I inched my arm around Sylvia Horton's shoulders at the Bugs Bunny Club. I was remembering that when Snow White said, "Excuse me, sir. Do you need help with your walker?" Prince Charming mumbled, "No thanks, I got it." I held to my walker and watched as Snow White, with her latte and spiked heels, strolled back into her own story.

A Quick Visit With Lillian

I dropped by hospice for a quick visit with Lillian before meeting Bill Martin at Jason's Deli. "I'm tired," she said. I took a breath, tried to feel her tiredness, take it in as my own, but a wind-blown branch that clicked and scratched at her window distracted me. I asked if she had written any poems lately. She said, "I'm cold." I found a blanket and tucked it tight around her. She picked bits of wool from it and rolled them between her fingers into little balls. We sat for a while, then she said, "I'm bored. Hold my hand." I checked my watch, but held her hand and tried not to think about the thick corned beef on rye I was going to have at Jason's. And there we were, two friends sitting together holding hands, finishing up. Then she died. The nurse came. Her fingernails were bright red and long. The branch clicked and scratched at the window. "You can let go of her hand now," the nurse said. The air came undone. I couldn't catch my breath.

Afraid of Death

I'm afraid of death—afraid of going to sleep and not waking up; afraid of taking a bite out of some sidewalk and knowing the instant before I die that people are stepping over me; afraid of being the source of the odd odor coming from my apartment.

I have noticed that people who die are forgotten. My children will remember a few stories, their children might recognize my picture, and their children will know me, if at all, as a hollow square on their genealogical tree. I worry about the poetry I want read at my memorial and who will spread my ashes.

I wonder about the people who might be present to honor my demise. No, present is not enough. I want *fully* present people with sad but enchanted faces. I think about what I might do to attract more and sadder people, how I might arrange to have my memorial video distributed to those who missed the first show.

I'm concerned about not believing in an afterlife and I stay alert for signs—a small burning bush, a lost sock suddenly appearing. I worry that people who dream up places like heaven and hell are people with questionable aesthetics. I don't want to spend eternity surrounded by bad taste.

What I really want is my friends, a small room, some books, writing materials, and a way to make coffee. Come to think of it, what I really want for all eternity is something close to what I have now.

✧

Last Lap: Molly's Exorcisms

Now that the finish line is in sight, I find myself looking for the Big Bearded Guy waving his checkered flag, a monumental smile on his face, eager to give me the biggest gold- and diamond-studded trophy ever. If not that, I'd settle for a certificate of participation. Or maybe a bumper sticker for my kids: "Proud Child of a Father at Hard Knocks Elementary."

Truth is, I'm trying to make my last lap a good one to make up for the considerable number of bad ones. Maybe it's too late, but I'm trying to become a more loving and generous person. My dog, Molly, is my teacher. She routinely performs exorcisms on me with her watery eyes and magic tail. A few months ago I became a serious devotee of hers. One long love-gaze from her before I make coffee opens the creaky old door of my heart just a crack.

This morning, after a long and loving session, Molly watched me take my first sip of coffee. Something was different. Sunrise and oranges spilled over my tongue. Warmth caressed my throat. I looked into my cup and saw nothing but my reflection. I took another sip. Summer mornings. Slow gliding swans. And Molly just sat there, tail moving back and forth. I swear she was smiling.

Meadowlark Lemon

Rosa and I sometimes meet at our mailboxes and talk. She talks about her lemon tree, how well it's doing this year. She mentions her "boys" who will come soon to fix her roof, hoe her weeds, and pick her lemons.

In her driveway there's a rusted-out car with flat tires and an old rowboat. "My boys will take the car away," she says. "But I'll keep the rowboat. I may want to row away from here some day."

I mention how late the mail delivery is getting, the desert light this time of evening, my son the chef in Seattle.

We never talk about the fact that soon Rosa and I will die, she from pancreatic cancer, me from ALS. Her skin is yellow. My legs are almost gone. It's getting harder to breathe. Last evening when I went to get my mail, she was sitting in her rowboat. "Come," she said. She held up a glass. "I made lemonade." I sat next to her. We drank lemonade.

Night came. A sliver of moon, the scent of a mowed lawn. Porch lights glowing, televisions flickering in neighbors' windows. "Where we going?" I asked. "We're here," she said. "We're floating on a deep lake, surrounded by trees."

We floated for a while before she said, "Once, I met Meadowlark Lemon who played for the Globetrotters. My boys liked him. You ever heard of him?" I confessed I hadn't but I liked the name.

"He's dead now," she said. The sound of a motorcycle sputtered a few blocks away. Then silence. "My boys ain't coming," she said. I said my son wasn't coming either. She took a sip of lemonade and said, "Say it, say *Meadowlark Lemon* real slow like a lullaby." So I did. Then she repeated it: *"Meadowlark Lemon."*

After that we sat for a long time, bobbing up and down on our deep lake of understanding.

✧

Part II

Cultivate a boundless love towards all beings...
and towards the entire world....

—Gautama Buddha

From *Karaniya Metta Sutta:*
The Discourse on Loving-Kindness

Lava Lamp

After I didn't die and flunked out of hospice a decade ago, it occurred to me that I had never owned a lava lamp. I wanted one and soon. I checked eBay. Nothing. But Amazon had dozens, all different colors and shapes. A silver one with blue water and yellow lava blobs arrived two days later. I sat in my bed watching my lamp. No gusto here, no driving ambition, just those slow-moving yellow blobs of all sizes rising, sinking, moving up and down, softly colliding, changing shapes.

And I could smell patchouli oil and weed, and the Beatles were singing "All You Need Is Love." I took a little blue pill and paid attention to my mouth and throat as I swallowed. I crossed my left leg over my right one, took it back, and crossed it again. Amazing how the body moves—sliding, rising, sinking, always changing. Even my fingers that held a glass of water. I liked looking at them.

Then I heard Peg Duncan's laughter that time at the drive-in movie when her skirt got stuck in my zipper. She'd been dead for twenty years but I still kept the Barnes and Noble gift certificate she gave me. I watched the lava lamp and remembered her. I was big-eyed and smiling because I was still here and the thing that made most sense were those yellow bubbles floating in that womb of blue water, and I thought: from now on, it's all gravy, every gesture, one of love.

✧

Maxine's Story About Alice the Hen

I don't have time for formalities. I just pick up my food, find someone who looks interesting, and start talking. That's how I met Hackmuth last winter at the Salvation Army. I liked his look—wild gray hair, bushy gray beard, and eyes that were about to pop out of their sockets.

I told him that when I was ten, I had a pet hen named Alice, a Rhode Island Red with orange feathers, who thought she was a rooster. Every morning I'd wake up early enough to watch her strut about on her pre-sunrise inspection, head bobbing this way and that, stopping to scratch and peck at something before she hopped up on her coop.

I paused, waiting for Hackmuth to look up, maybe give me a wink or something, but he didn't. So I went on.

Once Alice was on top of her coop, she'd raise her head to the sky, flap her wings, and let it rip, not a crow exactly but something between a bad cough accompanied by a sneeze and the screech of brakes that sounded exactly like the brakes on my Daddy's old truck when he stopped at the gate the day he left us. Then, after Alice finished making her sound, she'd hop down and strut a little more before taking a few sips of water from the trough.

By this time, Hackmuth was eating his fruit cocktail. And I was relieved to see that he could move. I didn't fancy a man dying on me before I finished telling my story. The ending was the best part.

I said, Alice's call was as inspirational as any sermon I ever heard any Salvation Army minister preach and as formative of my soul as all the readings I'd done from the Bible. It was Alice's own sermon preached in her own voice, I said, a voice that still lives inside me, that tells me it don't matter who you are or how much noise you make, you are entitled to fling open those heavy gates that imprison you and sing your own song. That's what I tell anyone who'll listen, I said. Sing out brother, sing out sister. Don't hold back nothing.

Hackmuth took a last bite of his fruit cocktail and looked at me with those funny eyes of his. So I crowed at him. And that was the beginning of our friendship.

The Wink

Helen and Hank had slowed down. Hank watched too much TV. Helen was stooped and shuffled when she walked. But one day she asked for some boards, nails, a hammer and saw. She said she wanted to build something. Hank asked what she intended to build. "I don't know," she said, "just something, maybe a dog house." Hank reminded her that they didn't have a dog, and at their age it would be cruel to get one. She shrugged and began to saw.

Hank went in the house to watch a game, but Helen's grunts and hammering distracted him. A few hours later she had finished her first dog house. It was shaky and leaned to the left. A breeze would have knocked it over. Now, two months later, they have six, all of them fragile and weak but clearly dog houses. She's still at it. They could end up with a yard full of dog houses.

The miracle is, Helen's standing straighter and she's stopped shuffling. After she finishes for the day, she comes in all sweaty and proud. She makes glugging sounds when she drinks water and wipes her mouth with the back of her hand. Today she winked at Hank. That did it. Sometimes all you need is just a glimpse of joy, and love comes surging back.

Another Reason to Read Poetry

After their thirtieth anniversary, marriage became a slow crawl to nowhere for Henry and Ruby. They couldn't afford a divorce or marriage counseling, so to pass the time and maintain a scrap of civility, they began reading poetry to one another before sleep. At breakfast, they had tea and cinnamon toast, with a poem or two by Billy Collins. A month passed. They read in the evening, too. Ruby was puzzled when she noticed that her blue cup, the one with a chipped rim, made her feel...well...joyful. Henry discovered that frost no longer formed on their bedroom window. After three months, all their worn and wrinkled *what-ifs* and *if-onlys* folded themselves one day, marched down the hall, and leaped into the linen closet. A year passed. Winds whispered happy little songs. Trees talked to Henry and Ruby in different shades of green. A decade flew by. Their love has ripened so much that the fruit is about to fall from the tree. But they have no time to worry about that because this evening they will share sugar cookies and a pot of tea with Mary Oliver, and they will celebrate the miraculous first flight of a redbird chick who didn't even know it had wings.

Crippled Cricket

At the bottom of my sink, a tiny cricket was trying to hop out. One of its big legs was missing, one that helped power its hop. But, not unlike Sisyphus, it kept trying to escape its porcelain prison. Finally, I gave it a boost. It landed on the floor. I thought of stepping on it to put it out of its misery, but it had managed to pull itself under the refrigerator, from whence I heard the teeniest of chirps.

The month that followed was like drinking disaster from a fire hose. London had another terrorist attack, and Hurricanes Irma, Jose, and Maria roiled. Mexico City fell to a 7.1 earthquake, Puerto Rico was devastated again, our President threatened to incinerate North Korea, and a gunman shot more than 500 people in Las Vegas.

The cricket showed up again last night, still one-legged, still hopping around in circles. It perched on the edge of the sink. The phone rang and when I looked back, the cricket was in the sink, hopping and falling back, hopping and falling back, over and over again. It seemed to be a born sink-hopper. *We are who we are*, I thought, each fulfilling our own destiny. And I left it there in the sink. This morning there was another high school shooting. The cricket was gone. I listened for a long time but didn't hear its chirp. I choose to believe it made a clean escape.

Earthquake

Buildings in shambles, air filled with dust and grit. "Over here," someone calls. And we all converge on that spot. "No—here!" another voice calls. And we go there. We listen but can't make it out. A man heaves a slab of concrete aside. We claw at the wreckage. Some of us cry, some pray, some are overcome with hysterical laughter. We stop to see if the voice is still there. It is, but weaker. We peer through broken windows and into dark places, toss aside broken doors and shattered glass. Some of us are firm-jawed and determined, some old and barely able to move. Then, each of us in our own time stops and stands still, listening for a long while, and there they are, our own small voices.

Skipping

After our umbrella broke, we walked all afternoon in the rain. Didn't matter where. Laney looped her arm in mine. We swayed and bumped hips. We were so in love, we could have been walking barefoot over sharp stones and not have known it. She skipped ahead. She was always skipping ahead. She stopped, reached up into the rain, opened her arms and whirled around. Then she skipped back and hugged me, all wet and close in that black top and green skirt. And it felt as though everything was happening for the first time, the rain, her laughter. And I knew I was the happiest I'd ever been.

This morning on my walk I met a young couple in love. "Beautiful day, isn't it?" she said. All I could manage was a tip of my hat as I wondered if I should warn them to hold on to what they were feeling, not to count on anything that good lasting. But I didn't. They'd find out soon enough. I sat on a bench for a while, watched a leaf floating in a puddle. And I thought of Laney, how she skipped ahead...and ahead.

Since Your Memorial

for Mayflower

A chill has set in. The weatherman predicts snow. I covered your plants and let the kitchen faucet drip to prevent the pipes from freezing. And I moved Molly from the garage to the laundry room. Just in time, too. She gave birth to four pups last night. Yesterday I watched the Super Bowl and ate way too much guacamole. This coming Thursday the Winter Olympics begin. At the end of the month, March Madness kicks in, and after that, the NBA. Who wins is not important. I envy those who are part of a team, the huddles and celebrations, the feel of human contact, the connection players must feel. Sleep doesn't come easy these days. In the middle of the night, I slipped out of our bed and checked on Molly in the laundry room. She looked up at me like she wanted to know where you were. Her pups lay in a tangled pile. They nuzzled and pushed and whined to get closer to her. I watched them for a long time. It seemed like a perfect night to build a fire, sip some wine, and be close to you on our old sofa while we talk about art and poetry, and that thing we call soul. I couldn't go back to our empty bed so I turned up the heat, sat on the floor next to Molly, and stroked her head while the two of us watched those pups.

Making a Deal With God

God, You have to understand. For a while, I really believed I had been chosen and convinced myself that I was a minor saint. My ecstatic insights astonished me. I was pure love. I loved beggars and criminals and toads and sand and bark on trees. I had to tell the world about Your gifts. And a few saw something special in me, which was very confirming. Then suddenly my saintliness vanished.

For a while I faked it—lifted lines from Gibran, Mother Theresa, Moses. But I came to suspect they faked it too. Gibran died bitter and disillusioned. Mother Theresa, racked with doubt, faked her faith all those years. And I suspect all that *loving your neighbor* and *not coveting other's wives* wasn't really Yours, but just the delusions of a demented old man who had no teeth and still liked to bite.

You see, I understand now: The unknowable is Your realm, and You get upset when we humans dare to think we know and comprehend anything, much less Your nature. I understand that a kind of earned ignorance is the best we can hope for—not stupidity, just a golden question mark that comes after years of agonized tries to make sense of things. I understand that finally embracing the gift of not-knowing is true grace.

As You obviously know, I'm back to being human again—doing my laundry, eating my Cheerios, judging others, hating most politicians, coveting wives—the whole human disaster. So, God, should You exist, even in ways that are beyond comprehension, here's my proposal: Grant me one more year of being me, and I'll stay on my side of the fence—no more ecstatic insights, no more thinking I actually know something. Hey, I'd be willing to consider a counter-proposal. But that's not going to happen, is it? See, I get it.

✧

Prayers

When Ted was sacked from his job at Pella Windows, he was afraid to tell his wife. He drove all day on the back roads of Iowa and found himself in a small town surrounded by cornstalks and blowing hot dust. He parked in front of a place with a Budweiser sign, walked up some wooden steps, pulled his hoodie over his head, and went in. The screen door slapped behind him. Nobody looked up. Three old men sat in a dusty corner as if they had finally mastered the art of waiting. One was telling a story about a horse that couldn't swim, how he had watched that horse flail about in the middle of a river until it drowned.

A woman, not old but worn out, stood behind the bar, arms braced. "Welcome to the end of the road," she said. "It ain't the classiest of places but it's all you got." Ted ordered a draft. Behind her, next to the cash register, was a religious candle of some sort. He asked the woman if she was Catholic. "Nope," she said. "I worship at the shrine of Jim Beam." She said the candle belonged to her son. She showed Ted a prayer that was inscribed on the candle. "It's called *Prayer to the Virgin Mary as the Untier of Knots*," she said. "He prayed that prayer right up to his last amen." Ted told her that he had a few knots that needed untying. She held out the candle. "Take it. It's yours," she said. "Maybe my boy pushed it right up to the edge. Maybe one more prayer will do it."

the slot machine whirls
two cherries and a horseshoe
he drops another coin

When Ted left, the old man was telling his horse story again like no one had heard it before. Outside, he put the candle on the seat, started the engine, and headed home. He would call his wife when he got in range.

heads bowed everywhere
looking for answers
on their smart phones

Lazarus Ponders His Resurrection

I heard a voice. *Lazarus, come forth!* My feet were cold, but I managed to wiggle my toes. Flickers of warmth moved up my legs, my torso, my neck and face. I peered through dusty light at silhouettes of people standing nearby. A woman helped me remove the sheet that bound me. *What's going on?* I whispered. "You died," she said. She pointed to a young man. "And that one resurrected you with his words. He made a miracle." I said nothing but wondered why a young man with such powerful words couldn't also give me a set of good teeth, take care of my limp, and heal the boil festering on my neck. As far as I could tell, I was the same miserable me I was before resurrection. "You must spread the word," the woman said. "What word?" I said.

Even though I spent a week thinking about resurrection, my thoughts were the same as before I died. *The olives are small this year. Should I even bother picking them? This aching tooth is killing me! Why wasn't I invited to the wedding festival like everyone else?* And gawkers, so many gawkers coming to stare at me. The only thing I could figure was, maybe living is about learning to suffer and, of course, to suffer you need a body. So that's the message I gave gawkers. It didn't go over all that well.

The young man left. I heard they put him on the cross and three days later he self-resurrected and went to a nice place called heaven. This made me wonder why I didn't go to this nice place also. On the cross the young man said something about forgiving us because we don't know what we're doing. He got that right. We don't have a clue. If he ever shows up here again, I'll ask him about this resurrection business. Between you and me, I don't see much good in it.

✧

The Guard Light

Sam's wife, Millie, died a month ago, and he installed a guard light. Hackmuth worries that it will send Sam's intruders into his, Hackmuth's, back yard which does not have a guard light. Worse, Sam's light is so bright that Hackmuth keeps popping awake thinking it's morning. A pillow over his head doesn't work. Too hot. And he can't afford a curtain. At 6 a.m., he sits on the edge of his bed, limp from fatigue. He calls and asks Sam if he wants to grab a senior coffee. But he tries to be diplomatic. He makes the mistake of asking Sam how he's doing. Sam tells him he misses Millie. Sam asks Hackmuth if he might want Millie's bowling ball, considering how much Hackmuth liked bowling and all. So, Hackmuth, who has never been bowling, says, "Sure," and slips in a comment about the bright guard light. And Sam says, "Damn thing keeps me awake. Millie wanted it for years. I never got around to it. So, after she died, I put it up, like a candle or whatever."

Back home, Hackmuth installs a curtain from Goodwill that he traded Millie's bowling ball for and wonders how long grief takes. And, for a while at least, he vows to remember there's something to be said about those rare times when he manages to keep his mouth shut.

✧

Earl and Ellie Watch the God Channel

For a long time, Earl and I watched TV together. Normal stuff: *Dancing with the Stars, Wheel of Fortune,* and my favorite, *The Bachelorette.* Then Earl found the GOD channel. It claimed to broadcast world-class anointed, prophetic, and supernatural content channeled directly from God by the International House of Prayer in Kansas City. He couldn't get enough. He cried, he prayed, he shouted *hallelujah!* Sometimes he'd sit up all night praising this and cursing that. Then one morning when I woke up, the TV was still on, but Earl was no place in sight.

I checked the garage, the storage shed, the bathroom. Finally, I hollered, "Earl, where are you?" And I heard his muffled voice coming from the TV room.

"I'm in here."

I looked behind Earl's chair, the sofa, in the closet. "Where?" I said.

"In here," Earl said. "Inside the TV. Get me out of here."

I got down on my knees and looked closer at the TV. And there he was, a miniature Earl sitting in a tiny chair exactly like his TV chair. "How did you get in there?" I asked.

"I don't know," he said. "I was watching a healing, and suddenly...I'm in here."

I moved closer and asked if he could see me. He said he could hear me but couldn't see me. "Figures," I said.

"What's that supposed to mean?" he asked.

"It means, Earl, that sometimes I feel invisible."

"Just because I can't see you from inside the TV?"

"No, it's bigger than that."

"How much bigger?"

And I said, "I don't know, Earl, just way bigger."

"Get the remote," he said. "It's on my chair. Did you find it?"

"Yes," I said.

"Then use the damn thing, Ellie."

So I flicked around the channels. "Doesn't work, Earl. Every channel is you, you, you.... Maybe if I unplugged the TV now. Maybe..."

"No, wait, don't unplug the TV. Maybe you should call a TV repair guy."

So I thought about that suggestion long and hard. Then I said, "No, I think I'll just pull the plug." So I did, and he made a little muffled "Noooooo. . . ." His image faded to a single point of light in the middle of the screen. There was a little sizzle, a *pop*, a *poof*, and Earl vanished. Next day I traded our TV for a new one, and the first thing I watched was *The Bachelorette*.

✧

Miss Adelaide, Substitute Teacher

She pranced in, wearing loops of rings dangling almost to her bronze shoulders and a rainbow-colored crinkly dress short enough to see her net stockings and black knees. She was carrying a washboard. "Gather round," she said.

We gathered round. "Listen," she said. She closed her eyes and played that washboard: *shoo...shoo-shoo—shoo-shoo...shoo-shoo-shoo.* Once she got the rhythm going, she soon broke out with "Just a Closer Walk with Thee," channeled straight from the Holy Ghost.

Even though the Church of Christ teachings did not allow dancing or even wiggling around, Tommy Anderson's body started bouncing, Mona Elmore's head bobbed, and Reggie Fowler couldn't control his foot tapping. Soon all of us bibled-too-much and baptized-too-soon third-graders were bouncing, big-eyed and free. If Keith Paterson hadn't shouted "Shit!" we might not have noticed when our principal burst in, pointed to the door, and said, "Leave, Miss Adelaide."

I'd like to see her one more time before I go, to thank her. Greg Lawton said he saw her washing dishes at Tully's Doughnut Shop. Sue Love said Sheriff Cooney caught her practicing Voodoo and ran her out of town. Seventy-three years have flown by and those twenty minutes of Miss Adelaide are still my Burning Bush, my sermon on the mount, and my first glimpse of the living waters of soul.

✧

The Loser

For no reason, a hinge came off my cabinet door. I couldn't fix it because my Phillips head screwdriver had vanished. I wandered from room to room certain someone had stolen it. But why steal just a screwdriver, why not the TV? I checked. The TV was still there. I opened the freezer and took out an orange popsicle, but a voice in my head said, *That's not what you're looking for.* I wandered into the garage. There in the corner was the driftwood floor lamp I made in woodshop for Carrie Masterson so many years ago. She had cried from happiness. We kissed under the bleachers. Then the day after graduation, she told me she was going to marry Ken Holbrook. She said I was a loser. A month later she and Ken stopped by in their U-Haul to return the lamp. All she could say was, *Our relationship wasn't in God's plan.* That's the last I saw of her. In all these years, I haven't figured out how I lost her. I was remembering this when I saw something at the base of the lamp. I couldn't believe my eyes. Right next to Carrie's lamp was my Phillips head screwdriver.

A Short History of the Banger

In the beginning, a few slimy cells slithered from the sea and eventually turned into bipeds resembling short, hairy humans with overhanging foreheads who had little to do but sleep, eat coconuts, and copulate. Then one day a particularly restless biped, let's call him Ork, grew bored with opening coconuts with his head and discovered something known today as a stone hatchet. Loosely translated, Ork called it his *banger*. Soon he discovered that in addition to opening his coconuts with his *banger*, he could also use it to open his neighbor's head, steal his coconuts, and, by default, inherit his neighbor's copulating partner whose name was Matt. (There were no girl names back then.)

But, as things go, Matt grew weary of servicing Ork and wanted a life she could call her own. She insisted they go into the *banger* business. Ork made them; Matt exchanged them for food, pretty sea shells, and other copulating partners. Matt also developed what she called a *double banger*. It had a rock on both ends of the stick. It cost more. And soon everyone, even the most wild-eyed and unstable, walked around showing off their bangers by smashing their neighbor's heads.

You know the rest: eons of banger wars, then spears, catapulted fire balls, guns, cannons, machine guns, Uzis, instruments of mass destruction, rape, pillage, religious wars, witch hunts, spouse abuse, atomic bombs, hydrogen bombs, smart bombs, and MOAB the mother of all bombs. The debate still rages regarding where evil resides, in the bangers themselves or in the hearts of those bipeds who use them.

✧

Lady Luck

With all these cars and guns and politicians mixed in with our own easy rage and stupidity, life is dangerous. Yet most of us get through with only a little damage. Vitamins help. Religion and fear do too if they don't kill you first. But most of the time it comes down to being on good terms with Lady Luck. All my life she has been good to me. When I was sixteen I should have died or killed someone when I drove full speed down the winding road from Lake Gregory to San Bernardino. Without her, I wouldn't have survived the rip tide in San Clemente or the time I dove head first into cement. She was working overtime when I received dispensation from the disasters of two marriages. Without her generosity of heart, I couldn't have raised two great children who gave the world five awe-inspiring children of their own. Late in my life, she even worked her magic to make sure I survived a stay in hospice. And recently, she figured I was ready and showed me the way to a deeper, all-encompassing love. And that's it. That's my destination. Time to get off the bus. There she is, under the street light, waving goodbye. Here in my ninth decade, it's hard to give her up. But it's time. I've had more of her largesse than my share. I wave back and watch her disappear around the corner.

Panning for Gold

Can't sleep. At the kitchen counter, I sit in front of a small white vase which holds spring's first iris. Next to it, a clear blue bowl is piled high with the last of this season's oranges. I stare through the glass and remember long ago on Route 66 a roadside stand with a sign, *Pan For Gold 25 Cents*. We stopped and a whiskered man in muddy boots dipped the pan in the sluice and showed me what hope looked like. When I found a small nugget and gave it to my mother, I thought I'd saved us from every bad thing. I wanted to stay forever panning for gold, but she said we couldn't afford another nugget.

Now I peel an orange, old and wrinkled but at its peak of sweetness. I sniff the peel, hold that sweetness on my tongue, and think of the time I made a list of a hundred things I wanted to accomplish before I died. But I confused the gold with the panning. Real nuggets, it seems, cost not a quarter but a life, a life that has produced the miracle of me sitting here with a newborn iris and a blue bowl overflowing with old sweet oranges.

Part III

A joy that's shared is a joy made double.

—English proverb

Bilocation

When my wife told me about Ruth Ann's invitation to her son's graduation from his 28-day drug treatment program, while she told me there'd be an exhibit of his art that he painted by submerging himself in black paint and rolling on butcher paper, and while she wondered if Ruth Ann's son's paintings might be reminiscent of Franz Kline's tonal contrasts, I was practicing bilocation, squeezing through the bars of my indifference to Ruth Ann's son and my basic distrust of all adolescents. I made a midway correction, turned sideways just a bit, experienced a mild sensation of breathlessness, then *poof*, there I was in Paris sitting on a park bench with a pole in my hand watching a little red whatchamacallit bob up and down in blue water while the wind of my wife's voice rustled the leaves at the top of trees. Of course my wife and I went to Ruth Ann's son's graduation. And of course we oohed and ahhed over his paintings and congratulated him on his new sobriety. But, I'm happy to report, I wasn't there. I was in Portugal sipping coffee at a sidewalk café.

Maxine Elaborates on How She Met Hackmuth

I don't have time for formalities. At the senior center, I pick up my food tray, find someone who looks interesting and start talking. That's how I met Hackmuth. He's not exactly the kind of friend you dream about; truth is, he ain't much of a friend at all, but at my age one has to make do. Besides, he had a lost-soul look that I liked—wild gray hair, bushy gray beard, ruddy face. He was staring down with sad, watery eyes that looked like they were about to fall into his dish of fruit cocktail.

I led off with one of my sure-fire stories guaranteed to get a conversation going with any old geezer. It was about Alice the hen. When I was a kid, I had this pet hen with red feathers, Alice, who thought she was a rooster. I'd wake up early enough to watch her from our kitchen window. I liked how she strutted about on her pre-sunrise inspection, head bobbing this way and that, clucking, stopping to scratch and peck at something important she saw in the dirt before she hopped to the top of her coop.

I paused, took a sip of coffee, and waited for Hackmuth to look up from his fruit cocktail, which he was still staring at, puzzled, like Adam in the Garden trying to think of his six-millionth name for some strange insect. I thought maybe he'd give me a wink or a smile. But he didn't take his eyes off that fruit cocktail. Some people have problems with canned fruit cocktail. They think the maraschino cherry is poison. But most of us here have eaten out of dumpsters. No red-dyed cherry will hurt us.

So I went on, adding a little more punch, working up to the big climax. Once Alice was on top of her coop, she raised her head to the sky, flapped her wings, and let it rip. You ain't never heard a crow like that. It sounded like a tiny dog with its head caught in a vise. Then, after she finished crowing, she hopped down and strutted around again, clucking here, clucking there, like she'd just taken her place in the natural order of things with her being on top.

By now Hackmuth was eating his fruit cocktail. I was grateful for that. I didn't fancy wasting my charm on a dead man. But he still didn't acknowledge my existence. So I wound up with a flourish. I said, Alice's call was twice as inspirational as any sermon you have ever heard. It was as formative of deep soul as all the readings I've done from the Bible. Because, you see, that crow of hers wasn't learned from no Learn How to Crow in Ten Easy Lessons book. It was Alice's own joyous sermon preached in her own voice, a voice that still lives inside me, a voice that tells me it don't matter who you are, or what crazy noise you make, or if you paint your hair metallic blue—if you speak your own truth, you fling open those heavy gates that imprison you and before you know it you are singing your own song. I moved in closer, inches from Hackmuth's face. So, sing out brother, sing out because there's only one person in this world that sings your song. Don't hold back nothing.

Hackmuth took a last bite of his fruit cocktail, paused, and looked up at me with those bloodhound eyes of his. So I puffed up and crowed at him again. It was a risk. You crow in someone's face, you never know what's going to happen. I've been hauled in for less.

For the longest time, Hackmuth just stared at me, exactly like he was staring at his fruit cocktail. And just as I was sucking in some air, fixing to crow at him again, he said "Do you want my maraschino cherry?" Well, you hear something like that, when someone offers you his maraschino cherry, it melts your heart. That cherry was the beginning of our friendship. It's been pretty much the same ever since. Me pitching hardballs, Hackmuth lobbing back maraschino cherries.

✧

Bud's Fantasy

The sky is clear, and an afternoon wind blows just enough to throw off my serve. My friend Ned calls Tucson *Paradise* this time of year. But today, I'd rather be ice-fishing in Minnesota, dropping my line in a hole in the ice, talking funny like Minnesotans do with all those *ya's* and *ya betchas*. You see, Barbara Grimes friended me on Facebook. There she was in a picture with Ivan Mitchell and their three grown children all dressed in bulky clothes sitting on five-gallon cans in an ice-fishing hut like she was doing exactly what she should be doing. But she didn't look at all like I remembered.

The real Barbara had perfect hair and teeth. I still picture her, high-stepping in her white boots with tassels and wearing that red-sequined short dress, as she tossed her famous flaming batons in the air. We would talk sometimes. I'd say, "See you later, Barb." And she'd say, "In your dreams, Bud," and then prance away.

So, when I met Ned for a drink, I asked him if he'd ever been ice fishing. He said he hadn't, and I said I hadn't either but I'd like to try it someday. Ned said it was way too late for that, that at our age we were pretty darn lucky to be here in Paradise. And all I could say was, "Ya, you betcha." I stared into my drink for a minute, then fished out an ice cube and chewed on it.

✧

A Smart Fly

in this the coldest winter
even a small ember
warms the heart

Stranded by a snowstorm, the man sits at his kitchen table, eating a glazed doughnut and watching a fly make repeated runs at the window. He remembers a few dumb decisions he made in his own life—that married librarian in Atlanta, the time he quit a good paying job when he didn't have a bed to sleep in. But, if that fly is dumb enough to want to go out in this weather, it deserves to live with the consequences of its decision. The man goes to the window and raises it. The fly circles, descends to the table, and lands on his doughnut.

A Rose for My Dharma Box

Years ago, when ambition was strong and angst was running deep, I bought a rose from a street vendor. It was almost dead. I took it personally and asked, "Why are you selling me a dead rose?" She said she didn't carry fresh ones. So I asked her to give me back my dollar. She said, "I also offer counseling services. You look like you could use some. That's another dollar." So, I gave her another dollar, and she told me that she rescued her roses from the trash behind the flower shop, that a rose has only one purpose and that is to make someone happy. She gave them a second chance. I waited a few seconds and said, "What about my therapy?" She said, "You'd be happier if you stopped trying so hard to understand everything." That evening I pressed the rose inside a dictionary. And now, many years later, knowing that I'll die soon, I look at that rose, breathe its old scent, touch its dried petals, and I feel happy. I have no explanation for any of this.

Mortality and Tacos

How could I have dreamed that one week from the day I heard the word *terminal* drop from my doctor's lips, I would be leaning over my old frying pan, inhaling the savory scents of garlic, olive oil, beef seasoned with tomato sauce, seasoned salt and pepper—and, yes, some fresh Parmesan—and know absolutely that I was making the best tacos in the best skillet that ever existed?

How could I have known that I'd be struck by the patience of things: chopped lettuce, avocados, strangers who hold doors open for me, my cat who waits for hours to lick my empty plate. And these diced tomatoes that I picked whole from my own garden, waiting so peacefully to fulfill their destiny in this, the best of all possible tacos.

How did it happen so suddenly that there was nothing on this earth that I wanted to possess? And at the same time, I was possessed by the desire to add just a touch of fresh parsley—and, oh my God, some melted Velveeta cheese—to this preeminent construction of gladness.

Joy-Bringers

Walking, for instance, tennis, naps, opening a can
of Campbell's soup, making love. I cling
to my joy-bringers—big laughers, a good self-pity
session, cooking a meal, eating out, fasting,
eating a healthy diet, popcorn with lots
of butter, puppies, my 20-year-old Kitty asleep
in my lap, dirt, a long shower.

I love plumbers and bikers who argue
about the meaning of life, discussions
with friends about garlic, my imagination,
pork rinds, Vietnamese soup, independent
movies, being a single parent, mindfulness,
fried Spam, getting really pissed at politicians
(I love that), flirting, hanging out
with angry feminists.

I shine my light into every nook and cranny
looking for the next joy-bringer—
heart hugs, massages, religious fanatics,
good teeth, black gospel choirs, an amazing
crack in an adobe wall, glass and brass,
those who help me carry
my briefcase and hold doors open,
a wise book that's also funny,
kettle corn, memories of martinis
at Cushing Street, the Rothko Chapel in Houston,
the waitress in Calhoun who asked,
You want white bread or biscuits?

Biscuits. These gravy days,
every one of them.

These no-rules days, these blue days,
these being-out-of-the-cage days,
these home-free and freely loving days,
my undeserved luck days when my joy-bringers
shine a beam on my heart. When my eyes well
from sheer gratitude. When I think of all
this joy and can hardly believe it.

Dancing

She's Pentecostal, a preacher's daughter. I'm Church of Christ. We're both forbidden to dance. It infects us with lewd thoughts. So, we sit on the junior high steps. We sit and watch the other kids dance. And I'm sure she's going to hell because she's not Church of Christ and because she's tapping her foot to the music, and in the Lord's eyes tapping is the same as dancing. As for me, I'm proud Jesus is watching, because I'm not tapping mine. I'm just watching the dancers and her foot.

Then, on its own, my foot begins to tap too. I tell it to stop but it won't.

We sit there, both of us tapping our feet. Then I feel her finger punching at my shoulder, and she says, "My folks are going to Bible study on Saturday. Would you like to come over, and..." She sorta raises her eyebrows. I'm thinking: *And what? And what?*

My breath leaves me. My foot's still tapping but otherwise I'm a stone monument to Christ's teachings. And finally she leans over and whispers one breathy word in my ear, "Daaaaance." On its own my head bobs to the beat. My foot practically leaves my leg. And that, my friend, marks the beginning of my long decline into sin.

On Saturday I ride my bike to her house, praying all the way for Jesus to give me strength to turn around, and to forgive me if I can't. But when I see hair down, bare feet, a flowered dress, and painted lips, praying ceases to be important.

She puts on a record, and something like I've never heard at church comes out, something that makes me itch and want to holler. "It's called Twistin'," she says. "Goes like this." She moves her butt back and forth and squiggles her foot like she's stomping out a cigarette.

I don't work my way into it—I jump and leap, land on my feet, and start twistin' my butt. She's looking right at me. And I'm looking back. We're twistin'. She stomps and lets out a high-pitched squeal, which to me trumpets the opening of heaven's door. She turns the music louder and screams, "Christ Almighty!" And I scream, too, because I'm twistin' and burrowing down a long dark tunnel into my own personal darkness. I'm scared the devil is down there, but I don't care 'cause I've never felt like this before, not even when I was baptized full immersion and rose from the water to see the golden light shining.

Then the music stops but we keep dancing, close now and slow, just swaying, hardly moving. I feel her heart, the heat of her breath fluttering on my neck, the wires in her bra, and for an instant I think about my preacher proclaiming how dancing leads to lewd and lascivious thoughts, because I'm having plenty of them and they're at least as good as a chocolate malted with whipped cream.

We move closer, our bodies weld together, and she kisses me with her painted lips, and I kiss her back a big one, and when our tongues touch, it feels like the flutter of angel wings and I think, *Christ Almighty, Christ Jesus Almighty. Thank you God, You and all Your angels in heaven.*

You Asked Me What I Wanted
You to Remember About Me

I said *everything*. Don't leave out anything. Remember every shoelace that came untied, my missionary work in Brazil, every puerile whisper, every peck on the cheek. Remember every loose-lipped, mouth-gaping, tongue-probing kiss, every sound of a great sexual drum marching us off that great cliff-diving leap into the ocean of orgasm. Remember every poem we read together, the cricket with the broken back in the motel in Elko, the wounded elk in Yellowstone that pleaded for its life, the koi we fed in Japan, the time I skydived onto the crest of Mount Everest and saved twenty poets from certain death. And before that when I made a lake of wine and turned tiny little fishes and dry loaves into a Bacchanalian wedding feast.

Remember the dress you wore in the rain in Paris, how the chill made your nipples burn with yearning. Remember the scents of fresh buttered rolls and coffee at that little bakery where we stopped after making love. Remember it all—everything—the totality of my soul and all it contained, all the little sighs of submission, all the swallowed screams of pleasure. And the laughter. Remember the laughter.

Impossible you say? Impossible to remember everything, you say? I've made it all up, you say, turned myself into my own myth. Well then, let me think.... Remember the time you wore that knit dress, brushed past the back of my hand, and whispered, *I love you*. That happened, didn't it? Or am I making it up? If so, remember this: Remember only that I love you.

✧

Just Before Sleep

In the haunting silence that comes with night rain, she spoons closer to his back and rests her hand on his thigh. Her breath moth-wings on his neck. Across the room she sees rivulets on the window pane intersect, stop, dart left and right, arrive and disappear. It seems important to her to understand, to discover order and purpose there, to see signs of courage or fate or helplessness.

But she finds nothing—no significance, not a hint of forethought, no rhyme, no reason why rivulets move here and not there, why she feels so much bliss one moment and falls terrified the next. It seems so perfectly imperfect—this moment just before she receives the blessing of not knowing and slips into the soft waters of sleep.

By what miracle
does the noise in us
become a song?

The Hum

I was old before I noticed it. And then I heard it in my roses, in lemons, a watermelon seed, stones, cement walls, my pillow. I told a philosopher. She said Pythagoras found it in the spheres, that Hartley called it *vibratiuncles*.* A musicologist friend said Palestrina's compositions echoed it. And the ground bass of Gregorian chants, the deep, chest rumble of Tibetan monks, the *Om*'s of chanting Hindus. A physicist friend said scientists found it in a martini olive and the rings of Saturn, in ocean tides and the moon, in icicles, garbage dumps, fog and ashes, in Triscuits and cheese. Imagine me, alone, wide-eyed, sitting in my backyard, bathed in the hum of joy, holding a bowl of humming buttered popcorn with lots of salt, maybe a diet Coke, listening to the stars, the song of elm leaves gathered in the fence-corner, the neighbor's barking dog, the blue hum of my rosemary bush. Not only that. I'm humming, too, all of me, head to toe. And I know this is the way I will be for all eternity.

[*See Footnote III, page 80.]

Virtue and Suffering

Long ago, a voice told me that if I suffered as Jesus did and lived a virtuous life, God would punch my ticket to heaven. It turned out that virtue wasn't my virtue, but the suffering part came easy from a series of bad decisions. I married an artist I didn't love, built her a studio, and before a year passed, she ran off with a psychotic Harley guy. She came home, went blind, and became an alcoholic—and for the next ten years I took care of her. I tried to think of this as earned virtue, but most of the time I was really pissed. Then, after a series of bad career decisions, I married an ex-nun who ran off with a linebacker for the Philadelphia Eagles. Now at 81, I have a friend I love. She is 83. We write and read poetry together. We make love, drink dandelion wine, and laugh. We make our own sauerkraut. We dance to Louis Prima and Keely Smith CDs. My human life has finally appeared in bold relief. I can't believe this goodness. It's so simple, this loving and being loved, as simple as holding hands while watching *Wheel of Fortune* or sharing Oreos and hot chocolate before bed. I may be short of virtue, but if this isn't heaven, it's close enough.

Shedding

Blossom after blossom,
petals fade and fall.
And we forget why
we bought our timeshare,
the cruise to Turkey,
and season tickets
to the ballet.

Veins in leaves
stop transporting sap,
shrivel and fall. Our delight
in film drops away. We donate
two shelves of self-help books
to Goodwill and give up walking
to Jane Fonda's CD.

Limbs turn dark, dry up,
are easily broken. We consider
taking a class in post modernism,
but don't. We buy two new lift-chairs.
Eating out is just too much trouble.
Peanut butter and marmalade
have never tasted better.

Only our stalks are left,
not beautiful to the eye but tall
and healthy enough to sink
deep roots. We embrace
our true and noble hearts,
the perennial flowers
that blossom there.

And finally we know—
what we have left
is all that we ever were.

Vietnamese Soup

Don't ask me to name my deepest feelings or tell you what fierce heat lies in my heart. Not today anyway. Today I rage with the unwanted passion of sure defeat, a manufactured man, constructed carelessly of twigs and leaves, and when I'm feeling this way, I find it useful to ask, what do I want one more time before a gale sweeps this foliage away? Could I use more knowledge and insight into the human soul? Not really. I don't make good use of what little I have. What I really want is one more bowl of Vietnamese soup. I want to steep myself in the steamy odors of basil, ginger, star anise, and the salty-sweet taste of Hoisin sauce. I want to feel the snap of fresh bean sprouts, the slithering smoothness of steamy rice noodles as I lift them into my mouth with chopsticks. And while I'm at it, I'd like a large window in the restaurant and a strong wind to make the glass tremble. I'd like to see my teachers, counselors, ex-wives, and self-help gurus lined up outside with their faces pressed to the glass, looking in with perplexed piety trying to figure out how I ever got to be this happy.

Cage or Lighthouse?

My body and an incurable disease have conspired to set me free. They're giving me another chance to learn what Death tried to tell me back when I was in hospice, that when your world stops spinning after a terminal diagnosis, there's a sense of receiving a reprieve from a life sentence. It's like being released from an old familiar cage and relocated to a lighthouse. I think of my old dog Molly who chose not to leave the back yard long after the gate had fallen down. And I feel regret at leaving this comfortable cage called my life. I'll miss my desk and my TV. I'll miss my friends and family. I'll miss our squabbles over whose turn it is to load the dishwasher and our wrath-and-envy sessions about the world falling apart.

In the lighthouse, with its view of forever, you know what's worth keeping and what you can let go. Your old coffee cup has more soul than all of politics. Ambition washes ashore, broken and covered in barnacles, and you know that the greatest danger is not crashing into the rocks but letting your light go out.

✧

Gratitude

In this morning's frost, light is everywhere. The lemon tree is glazed with it. If touched, each lemon will burst out laughing. A cardinal hops from branch to branch wrapping the mesquite in flaming red ribbon. Two doves circle and climb overhead bathing in blue light. A cactus wren perches atop the neighbor's saguaro, as if it knows exactly why it's here. On a day like this, we come awake and hear God ask if we're ready to leave all this. I answer, I am, but if I'm granted another day, nothing matters more than being here today, sharing light, all of us here sharing this light.

Back Matter

Every sun has to set.

—Arabian proverb

Footnotes

I. "Intro From the Publisher"

Pericles, as quoted in *Flicker to Flame: Living with Purpose, Meaning, and Happiness* (Morgan James Publishing, 2006) by Jeffrey Thompson Parker; paraphrased from Book II of the *History of the Peloponnesian War* (431 BCE) by Thucydides.

II. "Fame, aka Ginsberg's Last Soup"

Author's Commentary, 6 May 2015:

In the Seventies, Ginsberg and Ram Dass showed up at my crazy college for two weeks.[1] They stayed at my place. We prepared meals together. The first night Ginsberg wanted to make his "famous vegetable soup." So he did and we ate it with cornbread and honey and baked acorn squash. Long meal, lots of talk, and at the end lots of soup left over. So Ginsberg said, "Someday I'm going to be famous. Dan, you should freeze the leftover soup in ice trays, and ten years from now each soup cube will be as valuable as gold." We laughed and ate the soup for breakfast the next morning.

Years later, after Ginsberg died, I read an article in *The New Yorker*.[2] A friend who cleaned out Ginsberg's apartment after he died found two trays of frozen soup in the refrigerator and couldn't figure out what to do with them—eat the soup for holy inspiration, toss it, or have some sort of ritual goodbye. As I recall, he contacted [a museum] and donated Ginsberg's frozen soup cubes to them. As far as I know they may still be there—cold little metaphors.

Publisher's Notes:

1. Allen Ginsberg and Ram Dass were among numerous resident artists at Thomas Jefferson College in Michigan where Dan Gilmore was serving as Dean. During the summers of 1971, 1973, and 1975, the college hosted three National Poetry Festivals which attracted "dozens of the country's most honored and innovative poets...for workshops, exhibits, readings and other events, including such luminaries as Robert Bly, Allen Ginsberg, Donald Hall, Gregory Corso, Robert Creeley, Diane Wakoski, Diane DePrima, Galway Kinnell, Nikki Giovanni, Ishmael Reed, and many, many more."

(From "GVSU History," https://www.gvsu.edu/anniversary/history-colleges-history-1970-1980-27.htm, accessed on 19 February 2018.)

2. "Ginsberg's Last Soup" by Steve Silberman in *The New Yorker*, "Department of Immortality" (19 March 2001):

https://www.newyorker.com/magazine/2001/03/19/ginsbergs-last-soup

III. "The Hum"

Publisher's Note: The term *"vibratiuncles"* was first used by the British philosopher David Hartley in his 1749 tome, *Observations on Man, his Frame, his Duty, and his Expectations.*

Acknowledgments

Front-cover and title-page photographs: Box carved from mango wood by unknown artist(s).

Creative works appear in this book with permission from the author, Dan Gilmore. Of the 50 works herein, 28 are previously unpublished and 22 are reprints as indicated below. "*KYSO Flash*" refers to the online literary and arts journal at: www.kysoflash.com.

1. **"A Smart Fly"** is reprinted from Gilmore's chapbook *Just Before Sleep* (KYSO Flash Press, May 2015).

2. **"Afraid of Death"** appears previously in modified forms in Gilmore's books, *Love Takes a Bow* (Imago Press, 2010) and *Season Tickets* (Pima Press, 2003).

3. **"Billie Holiday, July 1959"** appears as a slightly different version entitled "Lady Day: July 1959" in *KYSO Flash* (KF-9, Spring 2018).

4. **"Bilocation"** is reprinted from *KYSO Flash* (KF-9, Spring 2018).

5. **"Dancing"** appears as a slightly different version in *KYSO Flash* (KF-7, Spring 2017).

6. **"Fame, aka Ginsberg's Last Soup,"** along with author's commentary and publisher's notes, are reprinted from *KYSO Flash* (KF-9, Spring 2018).

7. **"Gratitude"** is reprinted from the anthology *A Trembling of Finches* (KYSO Flash Press, January 2018), and first appeared in *KYSO Flash* online (KF-8, August 2017).

8. **"Just Before Sleep"** is the title piece reprinted from Gilmore's chapbook (May 2015), where it was adapted from "For Patricia and Roy" in *Love Takes a Bow* (2010).

9. **"Lava Lamp"** was first published as "After I Didn't Die" in *KYSO Flash* (KF-3, Spring 2015), and is reprinted here from a slightly different version in Gilmore's *New Shoes* (KYSO Flash Press, 2016).

10. **"Lazarus Ponders His Resurrection"** is reprinted from a slightly different version in *New Shoes* (2016), where it was adapted from the lineated poem "Lazarus and Me" in *Love Takes a Bow* (2010).

11. **"Making a Deal with God"** is reprinted from a previous version in *New Shoes* (2016), which in turn was adapted from a lineated poem with the same name in *Love Takes a Bow* (2010).

12. **"Massive Impermanence"** is reprinted from a slightly different version in *Just Before Sleep* (2015).

13. **"Maxine's Story About Alice the Hen"** is reprinted from the anthology *A Trembling of Finches* (January 2018), and first appeared in *KYSO Flash* online (KF-7, Spring 2017). "Maxine Elaborates on How She Met Hackmuth" is an embellished version of the story, written especially for this book.

14. **"Ménage a Trois"** is reprinted from *Just Before Sleep* (2015).

15. **"Miracles *(for Ted Kooser)*"** is reprinted from *New Shoes* (2016).

16. **"Oinks"** is reprinted from an earlier version in *KYSO Flash* (KF-8, August 2017).

17. **"Prayers"** is reprinted from a slightly different version in *New Shoes* (2016).

18. **"Shedding"** is reprinted from *KYSO Flash* (KF-9, Spring 2018).

19. **"The Gizmo"** is reprinted from a slightly different version in the anthology *A Trembling of Finches* (January 2018), and first appeared in *KYSO Flash* online (KF-8, August 2017).

20. **"The Joy of Being Lost** *(for JoAn)*" is reprinted from *KYSO Flash* (KF-9, Spring 2018).

21. **"Vietnamese Soup"** is reprinted from *KYSO Flash* (KF-2, Winter 2015).

22. **"You Asked Me What I Wanted You to Remember About Me"** is reprinted from an earlier lineated version in *Love Takes a Bow* (2010).

Alphabetized Guest List
for My Dharma Box Party

Edward Albee

Ellen Bass

Samuel Beckett

Rafael Bejarano

Robert Bly

Chief Bromden

Bill Bucci

Raymond Carver

Chekhov

Julia Childs

Marilyn Civer

Ram Dass

Fifi Day

Sam Day

Willard Day

Karen DeBellis

Mike DeBellis

Willem de Kooning

Karen DeLay

Dionysius

Conrad Driussi

Peggy Duncan

Margaret Dykinga

Einstein

Frederick Eisele

Audrey Lee Fatola

Lillian Fisher

Bob Fosse

JoAn Forehand

Helen Frankenthaler

Ada Jo Gilmore

Amanda Gilmore

Danny Douglas Gilmore

Hattie Bell Gilmore

Jennifer Gilmore

Leo Gilmore

Lucy Gilmore

Thurman Gilmore

Allen Ginsberg

Virginia Hall

Masha Hamilton

Patricia Harmon

Hermes

Trudy Hill

James Hillman

Hans Hoffman

Joe Hofmeister

Billie Holiday

S. L. Holland

Linda Hook

John Lee Hooker

Meg Hovel

George Jay

Holly Jebb

Janis Joplin

Frida Kahlo

John Kautz

Franz Kline

Ted Kooser

Steve Kowit

Dorianne Laux

Sam Lawrence

Carol Ann Lee
Heather Lindsley
Duncan Littlefair
Willy Loman
Bob Longoni
Terryl Mack
Clare MacQueen
Bill Martin
Lisa Martin
Mayflower
Joe McGrath
Tom McMahon
Cynthia Meier
Stella Miles
Henry Miller
Charles Mingus
Jamie Mitchell
Henry Moore
Mozart
Jackie Newlove
Mary Norman
Ronny Ossa
Andrew Periele
Fritz Perls
Roy Phillips
Picasso
Jackson Pollack
Elvis Presley
Kathleen Roberts
Carl Rogers

Eleanor Roosevelt
Alan Rubins
Nan Rubins
Rumi
Lou Andreas Salome
Bill Sandell
Sappho
Duncan Scott
Cheryl Seaton
Tobias Seltzer
Graeson Seminoff
Jeff Seminoff
Quin Seminoff
Bobby Shechtman
B. F. Skinner
Janet Smith
Tom Speer
Bernadette Steel
The Beatles
Jane Ellen Thompson
David Tyler
David Van Houten
Kurt Vonnegut
Nancy Wall
Walt Whitman
Cam Wilson
Dan Wolfe
Virginia Wolfe
Frank Lloyd Wright
Zorba

Alphabetized List of Works

✧

Author's Bio

Dan Gilmore is the author of a novel, *A Howl for Mayflower* (Imago Press, 2006); a full-length collecton of haibun stories, *New Shoes* (2016), and a chapbook of haibun stories, *Just Before Sleep* (2015), both from KYSO Flash Press; and three collections of poetry and monologues: *Season Tickets* (Pima Press, 2003) and, from Imago Press, *Love Takes a Bow* (2010) and *Panning for Gold* (2014).

He has won the Raymond Carver Fiction Contest, the Martindale Fiction Award, and multiple Sandscript Awards for Short Stories. His writings have appeared in *Aethlon, Atlanta Review, Blue Collar Review, KYSO Flash, Loft and Range, San Diego Reader, Sandscript, Serving House Journal,* and *The Carolina Review*.

"Happiest Black White Man Alive," one of Gilmore's flash fictions, was nominated for a Pushcart Prize, and was chosen by Pulitzer-Prize-winning novelist Robert Olen Butler as one of 55 stories for publication in *The Best Small Fictions 2015*.

In his time, Gilmore has been:

a fry cook,
a jazz musician,
a draft dodger,
a soldier,
an actor,
a minister in a Reno wedding chapel,
a psychologist,
a single parent of two children,
a college professor,
a dean of an experimental college, and
a consultant to business.

A video of the poet reading his work at The Rogue Theater in Tucson, Arizona is available on YouTube, which also includes readings of his poems by actors such as David Greenwood (who reads "Semper Fi" and "Prayer Wars"):

https://www.youtube.com/watch?v=Yfhb_0llrRU

Born in Oklahoma in 1937, Gilmore lives in Tucson, Arizona and divides his time between playing jazz, writing, and loving his two children and five grandchildren; his life partner, JoAn; and his cat.

Revised Obituary

I just finished writing my obituary. I'm not sure why. It's mainly a resume—man born, man dies, lived eighty-one years, dropped a few pebbles in the vast ocean of soon-forgotten achievements. I'm guessing the responsible part of me got carried away trying to convince myself that I've fulfilled my obligation. But I left out the part about the blind man I met who was listening to the rustle of trees in the wind and claimed he could hear snow sing. And the woman who cried when she read a poem that I left on her kitchen table one morning. I didn't say a word about the thrill of watching dragonflies celebrate their short lives with exuberant flight, and how I'll miss meeting Rosa at the mailbox. The thing is, resumes don't count for much. For me, what counts is the bucket that each of us carries from birth to death trying to fill it up, one grain at a time, and each grain is a piece of love. So, here's my revised obituary: His bucket is full.

Special Thanks

...to Clare MacQueen, writer, editor, publisher, and champion of all writers. Her good work continues to make us all better. This book would not exist without her talent, keen intuition, and unwavering support. I thank her for her laser eye, her good humor, her patience, and for occasionally sending me a box of Chapel Hill Toffee.

...to Tom Speer, long-time friend, teacher, and poet who for years has reminded me to avoid going over the top and to stay with my natural voice. Unfortunately, my natural voice *is* over the top. Sorry, Tom.

...to Steve Kowit, mentor, friend, tireless teacher and social justice warrior. You live on in our hearts.

...to JoAn Forehand, my life partner. Your love is like one of those trick birthday candles. Try to snuff it out and the flame keeps burning.

...to my OLLI students, who have blessed me with their appetite for reading and writing poetry.

...to the great laughers in my life. When I die, your laughter is the last thing I want to hear.

—Dan Gilmore
Tucson, Arizona
(March, 2018)

Notes

Made in the USA
Lexington, KY
28 August 2018